# Buffy THE VAMPIRE SLAYER

## CRASH TEST DEMONS

# Buffy the Vampire Slayer
## CRASH TEST DEMONS

based on the television series created by
### JOSS WHEDON

*writer* **ANDI WATSON**

*penciller* **CLIFF RICHARDS**

*inker* **JOE PIMENTEL**

*colorist* **GUY MAJOR**

*letterer* **AMADOR CISNEROS**

*cover photo* **KEITH WOOD**

*These stories take place during Buffy the Vampire Slayer's third season.*

Titan Books

*publisher*
MIKE RICHARDSON

*editor*
SCOTT ALLIE
*with* ADAM GALLARDO

*collection designer*
KEITH WOOD

*art director*
MARK COX

*special thanks to*
DEBBIE OLSHAN AT FOX LICENSING,
CAROLINE KALLAS AND GEORGE SNYDER AT *BUFFY THE VAMPIRE SLAYER*,
AND DAVID CAMPITI AT GLASS HOUSE GRAPHICS.

PUBLISHED BY
TITAN BOOKS
144 SOUTHWARK STREET
LONDON SE1 0UP

what did you think of this book? we love to hear from our readers.
please e-mail us at readerfeedback@titanemail.com or write to
READER FEEDBACK at the address above.

FIRST EDITION
AUGUST 2000
ISBN: 1 - 84023 - 199 - 8

3 5 7 9 10 8 6 4 2

*print valprint in italy*

# introduction

Buffy's senior year in high school, and enemies are coming out of the woodwork. After a brush with a flesh-eating modeling agency and a gender-bent rock stud, Buffy's ready to spend some more time with Angel and relax with the Scooby Gang. But her old enemy Selke* has been restored to all her nosferatu glory with the help of a twisted plastic surgeon, who's developing a talent for alchemy. Hellbent for vengeance against Buffy, Selke's staying out of sight while cooking up her master scheme.

Sunnydale's Bad Blood problem is about to get a whole lot worse.

*See *Buffy the Vampire Slayer:
The Remaining Sunlight* and *Bad Blood*

Art by DAVE STEWART

Art by JEFF MATSUDA and JON SIBAL
Colors by GUY MAJOR

'DELIA'S GONE

WHACK

HUH-UH-UH!

GOOD EFFORT. BUT NEVER EVER--

--TOUCH THE FACE.

I KNOW ROU LIKED TO CRACK THE WHIP. HECK, WE ALL LIKE TO HAVE A GOOD TIME, RIGHT?

HACK HACK

WELL I'M HERE TO INJECT A LITTLE FUN INTO THIS COVEN.

NAME THE THREE COLUMNS OF CLASSICAL ARCHITECTURE.

DORIC, IONIC, AND CORINTHIAN.

OH, I'LL NEVER BE ABLE TO REMEMBER ALL THESE FACTS.

TERRIBLY SORRY, MY FAULT.

RELAX, DON'T THINK. LET THE FACTS SPILL OUT.

CHECK IT OUT, WILL, YOU JUST NEED SOME ENCOURAGE-MENT-- GO, WILLOW! GO, WILLOW!

CUTE. NERDS CHEER-LEADING NERDS.

THAT'S GREAT, XANDER. PLEASE PROMISE ME YOU WON'T DO THAT ON THE DAY?

WE'RE ALL VERY PROUD OF YOU, WILLOW. LEADING SUNNYDALE HIGH TO THE QUIZ-BOWL FINALS, AN EVENT TELEVISED LIVE TO THE ENTIRE NATION.

I CAN FEEL THE PRESSURE FADING AWAY.

S'CUSE ME, IT'S ON P.B.S. A GUARANTEED AUDIENCE OF TWO, MAYBE THREE, LOSERS!

I'M SOOO NERVOUS, ISN'T THERE ANY WAY YOU CAN HELP ME, GILES?

WELL, IF I WERE UTTERLY IRRESPONSIBLE I'D ALLOW YOU TO USE THIS BROOCH OF THE OTTOBEUREN. BAVARIAN SHAMEN USED IT TO HELP THEM MEMORIZE COMPLEX SPELLS.

EWW, IT MAKES THE JOAN RIVERS COLLECTION LOOK TASTEFUL.

IT IS ALSO THE ONLY ONE OF ITS KIND. MAKING IT TOO PRECIOUS FOR GREASY FINGERS.

WE'RE UP AGAINST HORTON MILITARY ACADEMY. SIX-TIME WINNERS WITH A WEAKNESS FOR GUNPLAY AND STA-PREST UNIFORMS.

THE FINAL'S NOT 'TIL FRIDAY. YOU STILL HAVE A WHOLE WEEK TO BONE UP.

AND THERE'S LYLE, MILO, AND SARAH ON THE TEAM.

YEAH, THERE'S LYLE, WILL.

SO, WHAT'S THE DEAL WITH LYLE?

LYLE, AS IN "SCI-FI LYLE"?

WELL, LYLE'S... FRIENDLY.

THAT'S AN INTERESTING EXCUSE FOR A DRESS.

WHAT'S WITH THE FIXATION ON THE SKANKY VALLEY GIRL, ANYWAY?

WHO INVITED LYLE?

LYLE INVITED LYLE. I DON'T THINK HE GETS OUT MUCH.

--THINK THAT STRCYNSKI IS THE DICKENS OF THE NEXT MILLENNIUM.

I'M GOING TO THE RESTROOM. YOU CAN'T GO IN THERE.

--THE BREADTH OF VISION, THE--

SHE'S THE KIND OF TRAILER TRASH WHO THINK POPULARITY RUNS IN DIRECT RELATION TO THE SHORTNESS OF YOUR SKIRT.

WHO'RE WE TALKING ABOUT?

BEING POPULAR ISN'T JUST ABOUT GLACE LIP GLOSS, Y'KNOW, IT'S HARD WORK!

IS SHE SOME KIND OF MODEL? I'M SURE I'VE SEEN HER--

HEY. WHAT'S HAPPENING?

NOTHING. JUST HANGING.

DID YOU SEE THAT? SHE WINKED AT ME.

S'CUSE ME.

--REALLY A CONSPIRACY TO STOP THE SERIES AIRING. WHA!

QUITE THE LADIES MAN.

--BUT I DON'T KNOW ANYONE GLAMOROUS, SOPHISTICATED, AND SMART. HONEST.

I'M SO BORED OF BEING LABELED "THE SHALLOW ONE." THIS IS A GREAT OPPORTUNITY FOR AN IMAGE CHANGE.

CORDY, I HAVE NO IDEA WHAT YOU'RE TALKING ABOUT.

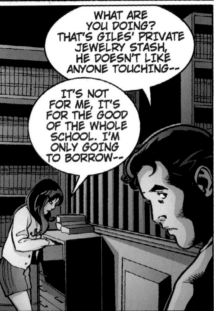

WHAT ARE YOU DOING? THAT'S GILES' PRIVATE JEWELRY STASH, HE DOESN'T LIKE ANYONE TOUCHING--

IT'S NOT FOR ME, IT'S FOR THE GOOD OF THE WHOLE SCHOOL. I'M ONLY GOING TO BORROW--

--THIS VERY UGLY THING.

WOH-OH-NO. YOU'RE NOT GONNA MAKE ME AN ACCOMPLICE TO--

YOU THINK JUST BECAUSE OF THAT, YOU CAN PERSUADE ME TO DO ANYTHING YOU WANT?

UH-HUH. NOW PICK OUT AS MANY GENERAL KNOWLEDGE BOOKS AS YOU CAN FIND.

HOW WELL SHE KNOWS ME.

QUIET NIGHT.

OOF!

HEY, WAIT! AREN'T YOU EVEN GONNA TRY TO EAT ME?

YOU'RE NO FUN!

AM I DELUSIONAL?

I ADMIT IT'S UNPRECEDENTED.

ZⁱZ ZNORK

CORDELIA, XANDER, AND ALL-NIGHT CRAMMING? WORDS NEVER BEFORE ARRANGED IN THE SAME SENTENCE.

I HAVE TO GO--

WHA--?

--IF I'M GOING TO COMPLETE THE QUIZ-BOWL TEST.

THIS IS THE PLANET OF THE APES, RIGHT?

SHE'S SERIOUS. A COMPLETE CHANGE OF IMAGE.

WHY?

I GUESS THE AIRHEAD LABEL HAS GOTTEN STALE.

YES, I ACED THE TEST.

I'M ON THE TEAM.

I'LL GIVE IT BACK AFTER THE QUIZ. NO. LISTEN, XANDER, I HAVE TO GO STUDY.

YES, BYE.

BEEP

PROTEIN, SEVEN POINT ONE GRAMS. FIBER, THREE POINT OH GRAMS. VITAMIN B-SIX, ONE POINT SEVEN MILLIGRAMS...

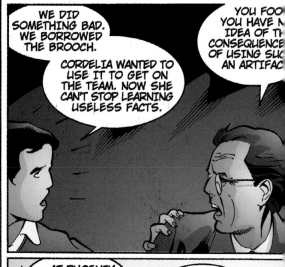

I'D REALLY APPRECIATE A LITTLE HELP RIGHT NOW. I DON'T WANT TO HURT HER.

AIEEEE!!

NNGTHHH!

YOUCH. GILES! THIS IS NO TIME TO PLAY ACCESSORIES.

ONE MOMENT, BUFFY.

GRARR--

LIKE THE BROOCH, THIS ISN'T FOR DECORATION. IT HAS CERTAIN MESMERIZING QUALITIES.

THERE.

I'LL PUT THIS SOMEWHERE CHILDPROOF.

CAN I GET AN ASPIRIN?

MEANWHILE.

DORIC, IONIC, AND CORINTHIAN.

HORT◯    ◯YDALE

07       12

CORRECT.

--WHEN SHE RAN SCREAMING...

...ALL MY NERVES DISAPPEARED. IT WAS THE WEIRDEST THING.

AT LEAST SOMETHING GOOD CAME OF THIS DISASTER.

CORD AND I HAVE TO RE-STACK THE SHELVES AND GENERALLY BE LIBRARY SLAVES UNTIL GILES HAS CALMED DOWN. HE'S NOT EVEN PAST THE SILENT, GLOWER-ING STAGE YET.

OUCH. YOU STILL HAVE THE SHOUTING AND GUILT-TRIP STAGES TO COME.

I HAD THE SHAKE, CHILI FRIES, AND CHEESEBURGER.

WE JUST SPLIT THAT FOUR WAYS?

THE VEGEBURGER AND SALAD WAS MINE.

BUT WITH THE TIP--

SIX TWENTY-FIVE EACH. CAN WE GO NOW? I HAVE A SPOT ON THE BRONZE DANCE-FLOOR WITH MY NAME ON IT.

Art by JEFF MATSUDA and JON SIBAL
Colors by GUY MAJOR

# LOVE SICK BLUES

SCREECH

HEY, CAN I GIVE YOU A RIDE?

SURE.

YOU'LL GO BLIND ...

THEN YOU WON'T BE ABLE TO SEE HOW BEAUTIFUL I LOOK IN THE MOONLIGHT.

SORRY, I MISSED THAT.

K-CHUNK

ARGHHHHH! HELLLPPP!

SLAYING TIME.

HELLLPPP!

HEL-GLUCK!

ELLIOT, YOU'RE STILL A DIRTY OLD TOERAG.

I HOPE NOTHING'S CHANGED, DARLING. I WANT IT TO BE HOW IT WAS BEFORE WE PARTED.

--WHICH IS WHY SHE KEEPS THE DOC AROUND.

JUST A LITTLE SIP, PUM'KIN?

I WOULDN'T, PET. YOU DON'T KNOW WHERE IT'S BEEN.

SELKE'S FEEDING UP HER MATES ON THIS SLOP?

YEAH, SHE HAS PLANS FOR THIS TOWN.

I'D LIKE TO WATCH, MY SWEET.

I KNOW, LOVE.

HUFF HUFF

TAKE THAT. AND THAT.

LET MY FRIEND GO, SLAYER.

HURT HIM AND I'LL HURT YOU ... BIG TIME.

KILL ... HER ... BUFFY.

ARRGHHH!!!

ANGEL! OW, THEY'RE DEEP CUTS.

WHAT HAPPENED? THEY USUALLY DIE SO EASY.

SHHHH. I KNOW, BUT THEY WEREN'T ORDINARY VAMPIRES.

YOU SAVED MY LIFE!

TODD?

THAT SHOULD HALT THE LEAKING.

DRINK. IT WILL HEAL YOU FASTER.

DON'T OVERINDULGE. I STILL HAVE WORK FOR YOU.

NO MORE DONOR HUNTING FOR ME TONIGHT.

NOT WITH THE SLAYER AROUND.

AND SINCE WHEN DID WE TAKE ORDERS FROM HER MONKEY?

DON'T DO IT FOR ME. DO IT FOR YOURSELF.

WHAT?

YOU *DO* WANT THE SLAYER REMOVED?

"THEY'RE SELF-RIGHTEOUS AND PARANOID ZEALOTS WHO VENERATE A SINGLE BONE FROM THE DEAD BODY OF A PREVIOUS SLAYER. THEY BELIEVE IT WILL PROTECT THEM FROM ALL SLAYERS."

I'VE FOUND MENTION OF AN OBSCURE VAMPIRE SECT, THE KIEN-JUS, HOLED UP IN TIJUANA.

ARE WE TALKING SOME KIND OF SLAYER KRYPTONITE HERE?

GET ME THAT BONE AND I'LL HAVE THE SLAYER EATING OUT OF MY HAND. COMPRENDE?

PACK YOUR SUNSCREEN, BOYS. WE'RE HEADING SOUTH.

--FELT LIKE TEN ROUNDS WITH A HEAVYWEIGHT. BUT WITH MORE BITING!

THIS IS A MOST PERPLEXING DEVELOPMENT.

I SAID SOMETHING SIMILAR WHEN THE BIG APE HAD ME IN A HEADLOCK.

MAYBE THOSE DEADHEADS HAD PUT IN EXTRA HOURS ON THE NAUTILUS.

THEY WERE NOT YOUR COMMON OR GARDEN VAMPS.

SUPER-SUCKERS IN SUNNYDALE?

NEVER A DULL MOMENT.

THIS IS UNPRECEDENTED. I TRUST ANGEL IS MAKING INQUIRIES OF THE UNDERWORLD?

UH-HUH. I ONLY HOPE THESE FREAKS ARE A ONCE-ONLY DEAL.

BUFFY, HI. CAN WE TALK?

S'OKAY, I'LL WALK FROM HERE. I WANT TO STRETCH MY LEGS.

SORRY TO BREAK INTO EVERYONE'S BEAUTY SLEEP OVER A NO-SHOW FROM THE VAMPS.

WELL, IF YOU ARE HAPPY WALKING, GOODNIGHT.

INCONSIDERATE CREATURES. I SHARPENED A DOZEN SPECIALLY.

RUSTLE

STEP OUT, WHATEVER YOU ARE.

UH, HI, BUFFY. I JUST DROPPED BY YOUR HOUSE TO THANK YOU.

TODD! I NEARLY GAVE YOU A PICKET-FENCE PIERCING.

SORRY, I WAS GETTING WEIRD LOOKS FROM THE NEIGHBORS SO I THOUGHT I'D HIDE.

I BAKED THIS ESPECIALLY FOR YOU.

LISTEN, TODD, I APPRECIATE THE GIFTS, REALLY I DO. BUT I DON'T WANT YOU TO GET THE WRONG IDEA.

I DON'T BLAME YOU FOR HATING ME, BUT I'VE CHANGED. I JUST WANTED TO TELL YOU WHAT A BEAUTIFUL AND AMAZING--

THANK YOU.

I JUST THINK--

IT LOOKS DELICIOUS. CAN WAIT TO TRY IT ANYWAY, GOTT GO NOW. BYE

SLAM

HMMMM. THITH ITH GOOD.

I COME BEARING GIFTS.

REALLY?

THE THREE UBER-VAMPIRES HAVE LEFT TOWN. MY INTUITION SAYS THEY'LL BE BACK THOUGH.

WSHHHH

... FROM THIS BROKEN BONE, MAKE WHOLE A NEW SLAYER, WITH THIS FACE ...

... TO DO FOR US THE WORK OF THE LORDS OF THE DEAD--SET, BELIAL, AND ERESHKIGAL.

FWOOSH

WSHHHH

IT IS DONE.

HI.

I REPEAT, "WE HAVE TO STOP MEETING LIKE THIS." JUST LIKE I TOLD YOU EARLIER AT THE WATER FOUNTAIN, THE PARK BENCH, AND THE GRASSY KNOLL.

I WANT TO TELL YOU SOMETHING.

DON'T. SAVE US BOTH THE EMBARRASSMENT.

BUFFY, I LOVE YOU.

TODD, YOU THINK YOU DO, BUT YOU DON'T EVEN KNOW ME.

I WOULD HAVE HELPED ANYONE IN YOUR SITUATION, SO DON'T READ ANYTHING INTO IT. YOU DON'T OWE ME ANYTHING, OKAY?

I JUST THINK YOU DESERVE SOMEONE WHO APPRECIATES BEING AROUND--

--YURK!

ARGHHHH!

LOOK, A DELICATE FLOWER FOR US TO PLUCK.

PLUCK YOU!

WASH YOUR MOUTH OUT.

YOW!

Art by JEFF MATSUDA and JON SIBAL
Colors by GUY MAJOR

MOVED UP IN THE WORLD, BOB? FORGOTTEN ABOUT YOUR BUDDIES?

GUYS, HEY, I WAS ONLY PLAYING ALONG WITH THE BAD BLOOD. I'M STILL TIGHT WITH YOU.

HRARRRRR

I'LL TAKE YOU TO SEE HER. GET YOU A PRESCRIPTION FOR THE NEW STUFF.

DON'T WORRY, BOBBY. WE HAVE A SAMPLE RIGHT HERE.

KRUNCH

KRAK

URGLE

HMMMM, GOOD.

DRINGGGG

I'M ALL READY TO DRIVE. I JUST NEED A SLAYER-MOBILE TO GET ME TO CEMETERIES IN DOUBLE-QUICK TIME.

WADDLING TO THE SCENE IN GILES' 2CV CRAMPING YOUR STYLE?

THE VAMPS DO POINT AND LAUGH. IT GIVES THEM A FALSE SENSE OF SECURITY.

EVERYONE GOT RIDES FOR THE TSUNAMI GIG TONIGHT? IF NOT, WE'LL BE SETTING OFF FROM WILL'S AT EIGHT.

BOYFRIENDS WITH TRANSPORT ARE THE BEST.

WHICH MEANS I'M GOING WITH YOU GUYS.

I'M NOT ARRIVING IN A VAN. I'LL TAKE MY OWN CAR. IT'S THE ARENA WAY OUT IN THE VALLEY, RIGHT?

YEAH. MOM'S GETTING ME THERE, SLAYAGE PERMITTING.

I'VE BEEN MAKING ENQUIRIES ABOUT THE TOUGH VAMPIRE THAT GOT AWAY.

GILES, IS THERE A NAME FOR THE FEAR OF KNOCKING?

WHAT HAS YOUR SURVEILLANCE UNCOVERED?

HE'S NOT THE ONLY ONE. MORE ARE CROPPING UP. THERE'S SOMETHING IN THEIR BLOOD THAT MAKES THEM SO STRONG. AND THEY SEEM TO BE GETTING THE BLOOD FROM A SINGLE UNKNOWN SOURCE.

THE REAL CONCERN IS REGULAR VAMPIRES ARE ATTACKING THE NEW BLOODS TO GET A TASTE.

QUITE EXTRAORDINARY.

SO THERE'S MORE OF THESE TOUGH VAMPS STALKING THE STREETS?

WE MUST FIND THE ORIGIN OF THIS BLOOD. ANGEL--

I'M ALREADY ON MY WAY.

WELL, THERE GOES MY R 'N' R.

NO, BUFFY, YOU'VE BEEN LOOKING FORWARD TO YOUR EVENING OF HORRIBLE NOISE FOR QUITE SOME TIME. I'LL ACCOMPANY ANGEL TONIGHT.

RR

--WE'LL NEED EVEN MORE FRESH RECRUITS IF WE'RE GONNA BE HUNTED BY PACKS.

CAN THIS SWILL GO OFF?

SHE'LL PAY, DOLORES. SHE'LL PAY.

HERE WE GO AGAIN.

WHOOMPH

HUFF HUFF

DARK SLAYER?

URGH.

GRRRRR!

GET THAT THING OUT OF MY SIGHT. NOW!

YOU TAKE CARE OF IT. I HAVE OTHER BUSINESS.

WHAT SHOULD I DO?

DUMP IT.

CAREFUL OF THE ALLIGATORS.

CLANG

SPLOOSH

BUFFY, SORRY TO LEAVE IT SO LATE TO CALL. IT'S BEEN A LONG DAY.

MOM, YOU SHOULD'VE BEEN HERE HALF AN HOUR AGO.

SORRY-- I WON'T BE ABLE TO GET AWAY FROM THE GALLERY UNTIL LATE. I'LL GET A TAXI HOME.

YOU WERE SUPPOSED T DRIVE ME T THE CONCER REMEMBER

I'M AFRAID YOU'LL HAVE TO HITCH A RIDE WITH YOUR FRIENDS. I CARPOOLED TODAY AND HAVE TO WORK LATER THAN MY RIDE. SORRY, BUFFY, BUT I HAVE TO GO.

OKAY, BYE.

DAMN!

CORDY AND OZ HAVE ALREADY GONE, AND GILES ISN'T ANSWERING. NO BUSES, AND I CAN'T AFFORD A CAB.

BUS SCHEDULE

ADDRESS & PHO

HMMMM.

NO, NO, NO--

BUT, I SWEAR, I HIT--

MEEP MEEEP

AM I LOSING IT?

HEY, LADY, MOVE YOUR CAR!

MEEEP

I'D BETTER CALL IT A NIGHT.

OOOH, SMARTS. YOU'LL PAY FOR THAT--

--DEATH- RACE GIRL.

SHOULD I CALL 911? THEY'LL THINK I'M CRAZY...

...AND ASK LOTS OF QUESTIONS. LIKE WHOSE VEHICLE IT IS.

WHAT AM I GONNA TELL MOM ABOUT THE DENT IN HER CAR? SHE EXPLICITLY SAID I COULDN'T DRIVE WITHOUT HER.

WHY AM I WORRYING ABOUT THAT WHEN I COULD HAVE ... NO. DON'T EVEN THINK IT.

BE BRAVE. JUST TELL THE TRUTH.

OR... MAYBE I CAN STRAIGHTEN OUT THAT LITTLE DENT MYSELF...?

FIRST RULE OF A STAKE OUT. CALL FOR BACK UP.

YAWWNN.

BUSINESS IS SLOW TONIGHT.

VERO?

WHAT HAPPENED TO YOU?

I HAD A FIGHT WITH A CAR. YOU'RE GONNA HELP ME EVEN THE ODDS.

I THINK I'VE MADE IT WORSE--

NOW YOU HAVE A MATCHING PAIR-- AT NO EXTRA CHARGE.

YOU?

YUP-- THE CRASH-TEST DUMMY FROM HELL.

HAD ME WORRIED FOR A WHILE THERE.

CRACK

YOUR WORRIES HAVE ONLY JUST BEGUN.

GUESS THAT MEANS YOU'RE ONE OF THOSE TOUGH GUYS?

GUESSED RIGHT.

KLONGGG

GONK

WHEC

TOUGH ... BUT NOT TOO BRIGHT.

GRARRRR!

WATCH THE PAINTWORK.

SORRY-- THE NEIGHBORS DON'T LIKE VAMPS. YOU'RE NOT INVITED IN HERE.

YOWCH!

WOH-OH!

WE DON'T WANT TO COME IN.

OOF!

WE WANT YOU TO COME OUT AND PLAY.

I WAS GOING TO ASK YOU SOME QUESTIONS--

--ABOUT WHERE YOU'RE FROM.

BUT I DON'T THINK YOU'D GIVE ME ANY--

--ANSWERS.

THUNK

WHAT'S THE RUSH, GUYS?

GRARRR

THE LAST PIECE OF SLAYER BONE, AND MY LAST CHANCE.

LET'S GET THIS OVER WITH.

WOOOOOOO

IMPRESSIVE FLOORSHOW, BUT NO CONTENT!

HUFF HUFF.

THEY WERE GOOD, BUT NOT THAT GOOD.

SOUND QUALITY SUCKED.

YOU MISSED A BIT.

WHAT DID YOU TELL YOUR MOM?

THE TRUTH.

PHEW.

SO, WHEN I'M NOT OUT SAVING MANKIND, I'M GROUNDED FOREVER, HAVE TO PAY FOR THE DAMAGE, AND ... HAVE TO WAX THIS THING UNTIL IT'S SO SHINY IT HURTS YOUR EYES.

WHICH IS WHY I ASKED YOU OVER.

GROAN.

C'MON, LIKE MOM SAID: "IT'LL BE FUN." LIKE THAT MOVIE, *KARATE KID*?

WAX ON. WAX OFF.

cliff richards

When *Cliff Richards* was trying out for a fill-in issue of Buffy, he had no idea he'd wind up being the regular artist on the book. He had such a natural grasp of the characters and such fluid storytelling that I jumped at the chance to hire him for the long-term job. He debuted in issue 8 of Buffy the Vampire Slayer, *which was reprinted in hardcover with added story pages as Dark Horse's* Supernatural Defense Kit. *He next popped up in the lead story in the* Buffy 1999 Annual. *After a short story written by Doug Petrie, which appeared in* Dark Horse Presents *millennial special and will be reprinted in the next volume of this series, Cliff took on the job of regular artist. The issues collected in* Crash Test Demons, *continuing the* Bad Blood *series, marked Cliff's beginning as Dark Horse's prime Buffy artist. As I write this, Cliff is still the star of our monthly series, heading into the epic* Blood of Carthage *story line. He's also trying his hand on a few other Dark Horse projects, including* Ghost *and* Star Wars.

Alongside the following interview we've run some of Cliff's tryouts, which landed him the Buffy job.

*Part of his audition was to redraw some pages of an old Buffy script, which had already been drawn by Joe Bennett. Ironically, the script he tried out on was for* Buffy #2 *(reprinted in* Buffy: The Remaining Sunlight*). That story featured the first appearance of Selke, the antagonist in* Crash Test Demons, *in a minor role. Though no one could've known it when he was trying out, Selke's ultimate fate, in the final chapter of the* Bad Blood *series, will now be drawn by Cliff.*

SCOTT ALLIE: *The first thing readers should know about you is that you don't live in the States. Andi, the writer of the book, lives in the United Kingdom. I'm in Oregon, and the colorist is in San Diego. Where are you?*

**CLIFF RICHARDS: I live in Brazil.**

*Where in Brazil?*

In Belo Horizonte, the third biggest city.

*Do you get Buffy on TV there? Did you watch it before you got the job?*

Yup. I watch the show whenever possible.

*Would you rather be drawing superheroes in tights, or chicks in armor with giant breasts, like other comics artists?*

I like drawing real people. That's one of the things I like about Alex Ross's work — the real humans in regular clothing. But I like superhero types, too.

*So you like Alex Ross. What other comics artists do you like?*

I like Adam Hughes, Stuart Immonen, and Rodolfo Damaggio. They've all influenced me.

*These guys are your contemporaries. Are there any older artists that have influenced you since you were young?*

The older artists that have influenced me are Alex Raymond, Lee Falk, John Buscema and John Romita Senior.

*Have you drawn superhero comics in the States?*

Yeah. I did a couple of comics called *Angel Heat*.

*What's your art background?*

I learned by myself. I tried art schools, but it didn't work. Besides comics, I do illustrations for educational books.

*Is that your regular job outside of Buffy?*

Yes, it is.

Most guys can't handle the schedule of monthly comics, but you can work a day job and draw these things, without ever missing a deadline.

**I just draw all the time.**

Why are you compelled to do comics? Doesn't the other stuff pay better?

**I've loved comics since I was a kid. I think all artists do. I love telling stories with pictures.**

Have you done comics in other countries?

**Just here in my homeland.**

What sort of books have you drawn there?

**I did a few short sci-fi stories.**

Is there a specific mood or atmosphere you try to get across in Buffy?

**Well, mixing the light, funny stuff and the dark, scary stuff is the key to *Buffy*.**

Are there many Buffy fans in Brazil? Do you ever do signings or appearances in stores there?

**Many people here are familiar with** *Buffy*, **but it's not like it is in the States. I don't know too many real fans. I've never done a public appearance down here.**

*You like working with your inker, Joe Pimentel. Are you guys old friends?*

**I like Joe's work a lot, but we just know each other by phone.**

*Does it drive you crazy when I ask you to redraw stuff?*

**I hate having to redraw anything, but it comes with the territory.**

*Sorry …*

# LOOK FOR THESE BUFFY THE VAMPIRE SLAYER
## TRADE PAPERBACKS FROM TITAN BOOKS.

**The Dust Waltz**
Brereton • Gomez • Florea
80-page color paperback
ISBN: 1-84023-057-6 **£7.99**

**The Remaining Sunlight**
Watson • Bennett • Ketcham
80-page color trde paperback
ISBN: 1-84023-078-9 **£7.99**

**The Origin**
Golden • Brereton • Bennett • Ketcham
80-page color paperback
ISBN: 1-84023-105-X **£7.99**

**Uninvited Guests**
Watson • Gomez • Florea
104-page color paperback
ISBN: 1-84023-140-8 **£8.99**

**Supernatural Defense Kit**
Watson • Richards • Pimentel
30-page color hard cover
comes with golden-colored cross,
"claddagh" ring, and vial of "Holy water"
ISBN: 1-84023-165-3 **£19.99**

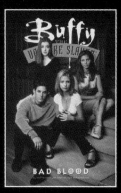

**Bad Blood**
Watson • Bennett • Ketcham
88-page color paperback
ISBN: 1-84023-179-3 **£8.99**

**Crash Test Demons**
Watson • Richards • Pimentel
88-page color paperback
ISBN: 1-84023-199-8 **£8.99**

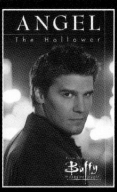

**Angel: The Hollower**
Golden • Gomez • Florea
88-page color paperback
ISBN: 1-84023-163-7 **£8.99**

*Coming Soon!*
**Ring of Fire**
Petrie • Sook
80-page color paperback
ISBN: 1-84023-200-5

**All publications are available through most good bookshops or direct
from our mail order service at Titan Books.** For a free graphic-novels
catalogue or to order, telephone 01858 433 169 with your credit-card details
or contact Titan Books Mail Order, Bowden House, 36 Northampton Road,
Market Harborough, Leics, LE16 9HE, quoting reference BCTD/GN

## BUFFY THE VAMPIRE SLAYER

**THE DUST WALTZ**
Brereton • Gomez
80-page color paperback
ISBN: 1-84023-057-6

**THE REMAINING SUNLIGHT**
Watson • Van Meter
Bennett • Ross • Ketcham
88-page color paperback
ISBN: 1-84023-078-9

## ALIENS

**FEMALE WAR**
(formerly Aliens: Earth War)
Verheiden • Kieth
112-page color paperback
ISBN: 1-85286-784-1

**GENOCIDE**
Arcudi • Willis • Story
112-page color paperback
ISBN: 1-85286-805-8

**HARVEST**
(formerly Aliens: Hive)
Prosser • Jones
128-page color paperback
ISBN: 1-85286-838-4

**LABYRINTH**
Woodring • Plunkett
136-page color paperback
ISBN: 1-85286-844-9

**NIGHTMARE ASYLUM**
(formerly Aliens: Book Two)
Verheiden • Beauvais
112-page color paperback
ISBN: 1-85286-765-5

**OUTBREAK**
(formerly Aliens: Book One)
Verheiden • Nelson
168-page color paperback
ISBN: 1-85286-756-6

**ROGUE**
Edginton • Simpson
112-page color paperback
ISBN: 1-85286-851-1

**STRONGHOLD**
Arcudi • Mahnke • Palmiotti
112-page color paperback
ISBN: 1-85286-875-9

## ALIENS VS PREDATOR

**ALIENS VS PREDATOR**
Stradley • Norwood • Warner
Story • Campanella
176-page color paperback
ISBN: 1-85286-413-3

**THE DEADLIEST
OF THE SPECIES**
Claremont • Guice • Barreto
320-page color paperback
ISBN: 1-85286-953-4

**WAR**
Various
200-page color paperback
ISBN: 1-85286-703-5

## BATMAN VS PREDATOR

**BATMAN VS PREDATOR**
Gibbons • Kubert • Kubert
96-page color paperback
ISBN: 1-85286-446-X

**BATMAN VS PREDATOR II:
BLOODMATCH**
Moench• Gulacy • Austin
136-page color paperback
ISBN: 1-85286-667-5

**BATMAN VS PREDATOR III:
BLOOD TIES**
Dixon • Damaggio
136-page color paperback
ISBN: 1-85286-913-5

## GODZILLA

**AGE OF MONSTERS**
various
256-page B&W paperback
ISBN: 1-85286-929-1

**PAST PRESENT FUTURE**
various
276-page B&W paperback
ISBN: 1-85286-930-5

## PREDATOR

**BIG GAME**
Arcudi • Dorkin • Gil
112-page color paperback
ISBN: 1-85286-454-0

**COLD WAR**
Verheiden • Randall • Mitchell
112-page color paperback
ISBN: 1-85286-576-8

**KINDRED**
Lamb • Tolson
112-page color paperback
ISBN: 1-85286-908-9

## STAR WARS

**CRIMSON EMPIRE**
Richardson • Stradley
Gulacy • Russell
160-page color paperback
ISBN: 1-84023-006-1

**TALES OF THE JEDI: THE
GOLDEN AGE OF THE SITH**
Anderson • Gossett
Carrasco • Heike • Black Beckett
Woch
144-page color paperback
ISBN: 1-84023-000-2

**X-WING ROGUE SQUADRON:
THE WARRIOR PRINCESS**
Stackpole • Tolson
Nadeau • Ensign
96-page color paperback
ISBN: 1-85286-997-6

**X-WING ROGUE SQUADRON:
REQUIEM FOR A ROGUE**
Stackpole • Strnad • Erskine
112-page color paperback
ISBN: 1-85286-026-6

## VARIOUS

**BATMAN/ALIENS**
Marz • Wrightson
128-page color paperback
ISBN: 1-85286-887-2

**PREDATOR VS
JUDGE DREDD**
Wagner • Alcatena
80-page color paperback
ISBN: 1-84023-021-5

**STARSHIP TROOPERS**
various
144-page color paperback
ISBN: 1-85286-886-4

**SUPERMAN/ALIENS**
Jurgens • Nowlan
152-page color paperback
ISBN: 1-85286-704-3

**TARZAN VS PREDATOR
AT THE EARTH'S CORE**
Simonson • Weeks
104-page color paperback
ISBN: 1-85286-888-0

All publications are available through most good bookshops or direct from our mail-order service at Titan Books. For a free
graphic-novels catalogue or to order, telephone 01858 433 169 with your credit-card
details or contact Titan Books Mail Order, Bowden House, 36 Northampton Road,
Market Harborough, Leics, LE16 9HE, quoting reference BCT/GN